IN THE CITY AND ON THE FARM

EUNICE K. CRABTREE

LU VERNE CRABTREE WALKER

DOROTHY CANFIELD

Illustrations by
TERRY TOWNSEND

California State Series
PUBLISHED BY
CALIFORNIA STATE DEPARTMENT OF EDUCATION
SACRAMENTO, 1946

printed in
CALIFORNIA STATE PRINTING OFFICE
SACRAMENTO   1 ed. 75M 1947

Stories To Read

In the City

On the Farm

TO CIRCUS

THE SCHOOL

THE LIBRARY

MAIL TRUCK

THE GROCERY STORE

THE MOVIE HOUSE

City Children

Billy lives in the city.
Ted lives in the city.
They live on Park Street.
They live in brick houses.

Billy's brick house looks just like
Ted's brick house.
Ted's house number is 16.
Billy's house number is 18.

Mary lives in the city.
Jane lives in the city.
They live on Park Street.
They live in a brick house.
It is a big, brick apartment house.
The apartment house number is 20.
Mary and Jane know the number
of their big, brick apartment house.

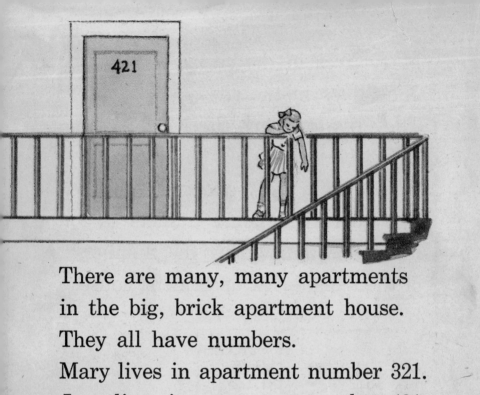

There are many, many apartments
in the big, brick apartment house.
They all have numbers.
Mary lives in apartment number 321.
Jane lives in apartment number 421.
Mary can find her apartment.
Jane can find her apartment.

City Streets

The big, yellow bus goes
by Billy's house. Beep, beep!

The big, yellow bus goes
by Ted's house. Beep, beep!

The big, yellow bus goes
by the big apartment house.
There is a bus stop on Park Street.
The children like to ride
on the big, yellow bus.

Many cars go by Billy's house.
Many cars go by Ted's house.
Many cars go by the apartment house.

Many trucks go by Billy's house.
Many trucks go by Ted's house.
Many trucks go
by the apartment house.
Honk, honk! Honk, honk!

The children do not play
in the street.
They play in Billy's yard.
They play in Ted's yard.
They play in the apartment yard.
They play in the little park.

The children must look and look
when they cross the street.
They must look for the yellow bus.
They must look for the green cars.
They must look for the red trucks.
They must look and look
when they cross the street.

There is a big policeman
on Park Street.
He tells the children when to stop
and when to cross the street.

The big policeman tells the cars
when to go and when to stop.
He tells the trucks when to go.
He tells the trucks when to stop.

The big policeman tells them
when to stop and when to go.

There is a big, green mail box
on Park Street.
Billy puts mail in the box.
Ted puts mail in the box.
Mary puts mail in the box.
Jane puts mail in the box.
All the children on Park Street
put mail in the big, green box.

They like to see the mail man
take the mail out of the box.
They like to see the mail man
put the mail on the mail truck.
Good-by, mail truck! Good-by!

There is a store on Park Street.
It is a grocery store.

Billy goes to the grocery store
for his mother on Saturday.

Mary goes to the grocery store
for her mother on Saturday.

Jane goes to the grocery store
for her mother on Saturday.

Ted's father is the grocery man.
Ted helps his father on Saturday
in the grocery store.

There is a movie house
down the street.
Billy goes to the movies.
Ted goes to the movies.
Mary goes to the movies.
Jane goes to the movies.
They go to the movies on Saturday.

Billy and Ted like movies
about funny animals.
Mary and Jane like movies
about little girls and boys.

The school is down the street.
It is a big school with a big yard.

Billy and Ted go to this school.
Mary and Jane go to this school.
Many children go to this school.

The library is next to the school.
Billy and Ted go to the library.
Mary and Jane go to the library.
They go to the library after school.

Fun at Play Park

One day Billy, Ted, Mary and Jane
went for a ride.
Mary's mother took them.
They went in the big, yellow bus.
They saw many signs in the bus.

Mary's mother said, "I see a sign.
I see a sign that tells
where we are going."
The children looked at the signs.
Then Billy said, "I know! I know!
We are going to Play Park."
Billy read the sign.
The sign said

GO TO PLAY PARK
TAKE THE CHILDREN TO PLAY PARK

PLAY PARK

The bus went on and on.
By and by it came to Play Park.
The children saw the Fun House.
They said, "Oh, look!
Let's go into the Fun House."

They saw the merry-go-round.
Mary said, "I want to go
on the merry-go-round!"

Ted said, "I want to go up
in the airplane!"

Jane said, "I want to go
in the little boat!"

Billy said, "I want to go
for a swim!"

Mary's mother said, "You may do
what you like best."

The children said, "Come on!
Let's all go into the Fun House, now!"
They all had fun in the Fun House.
Ted said, "Look at me!
I am short and fat!"

Billy said, "I am short and fat, too!"
They laughed and laughed
at the fat, little boys.

They went to the merry-go-round.
A ticket man said,
"Five cents for a ride
on the merry-go-round."

"See the horses," said Ted.

"See the yellow lions," said Mary.

"See the black bears," said Jane.

Mary's mother took the children
for a ride on the merry-go-round.

Billy rode on a black horse.
Ted rode on a white horse.
Mary rode on a big, yellow lion.
Jane rode on a big, black bear.
Mary's mother sat up high
on a brown and yellow tiger.

They rode around and around!
Around and around went the lion!
Around and around went the bear!
Around and around went the tiger!

Billy said, "That was a good ride!"

Ted said, "Yes, but it was too short!"

Billy and Ted went for a ride
in the yellow airplane.

Mary and Jane went for a ride
in the little red boat.

Up, up, up went Billy and Ted
in the yellow airplane.
Billy and Ted looked down.
They saw the girls
in the little, red boat.

Ted said, "See the little, red boat.
See little Mary and little Jane."

Billy said, "They do look little.
They look little from up here.
They look little to us."

Around and around and around
went the yellow airplane.
Down, down, down it came.
The boys jumped out.

Billy said, "Can you walk?"

Ted said, "Yes, I can walk
but I go around and around."

Mary and Jane came up.
They said, "We had a good ride."
The boys said, "We saw you.
You looked little. Did you see us?"
Mary and Jane said, "Yes!
You looked little, too!"

Mother said, "Do you want
to go for a swim?"

The children said, "Yes! Yes!
We want to go for a swim!"

Mother said, "Get ready.
Let's see who will be ready first."
The children ran to the bath house.
Billy was ready to swim first.
He jumped into the water.
Splash, splash, splash!

"Jump in," called Billy.
Ted jumped into the water
after Billy. Splash, splash, splash!
Then Mary jumped into the water
after Ted. Splash, splash, splash!
Jane jumped into the water
after Mary. Splash, splash, splash!
The boys had a race in the water.
The girls had a race, too.

Then they had a race in the sand.

Jane said to Mary,
"Put some sand over me!"

Mary put sand all over Jane.
Then Billy put sand all over himself
and Ted put sand all over himself.

There was sand all over Ted,
but his toes stuck out.

There was sand all over Billy,
but his toes stuck out, too.

There was sand all over Jane,
but her toes stuck out.

Mother came for the children
She said to Mary,
"Where is everyone?
Where is Ted? Where is Jane?"
Mary said to her mother,
"The children are gone.
All the children are gone."

Then Mary's mother said,
"Where have they gone?
I see toes here.
I see more toes there.
Come, children, jump up!
We must go home now."

But the children did not come.
Mary's mother tickled some toes!
Then up jumped Billy!

Mother tickled some more toes.
Then up jumped Ted!

Mother tickled some more toes.
Then up jumped Jane!

Mother said, "Come, children.
Get ready to go home, now!
Who will be ready first?"

Away ran the children
to the bath house.
The girls got there first,
but the boys got ready first.

When they were on the bus
the children said, "Good-by!
Good-by, Play Park! Good-by!"

On the bus Billy sat by Ted,
Ted sat by Jane, Jane sat by Mary,
and Mary sat by her mother.

Billy said to Ted,
"I liked the airplane ride best."

Ted said to Jane,
"The race in the water was fun."

Jane said to Mary,
"It was fun to play in the sand."

Mary said to Mother,
"I liked the boat ride best."

Mary's mother said,
"I liked the merry-go-round."

The children said,
"The merry-go-round was fun.
It was fun to ride on lions
and bears and tigers."

Ted said, "See that sign!
See the lions and bears and tigers.
Zoo animals do not look like
the ones we saw in Play Park."

The children said, "Please!
May we go to the Zoo some day?"

Mother said, "Yes, you may go
some Saturday when the sun is out."

COME TO THE ZOO

ZOO

Fun at the Zoo

One Saturday Billy and Ted,
Mary and Jane went to the Zoo.
They went with Billy's father
in his car.

When they were all in the car,
Billy's mother came out.
She gave Father something.
She said, "Take this with you."

"What is it?" asked Jane.

Billy said, "I know, I know!
It is a lunch for us."

And it was!
Away they went in the car.
By and by, they came to the Zoo.

Father said, "What shall we do?
Shall we have lunch first,
or shall we see the animals first?"

The boys said, "Oh!
Let us have lunch first."

The girls said, "No!
Let us see the animals first."

Father laughed and laughed.

Father took two sticks.
One was long; one was short.
He said, "Here are two sticks.
Jane may take one.
If she gets the long stick,
we will have lunch first.
If she gets the short stick,
we will see the animals first."

Jane took a stick. She said,
"Oh! It is the long stick."

"Good," said the boys.
"Jane got the long stick.
We will have lunch first."

Father got the big lunch box
out of the car.
"What a good lunch," said Billy.
"What a good lunch," said Ted.
"I like the lemonade," said Jane.
"I like all the lunch," said Mary.
"I have a good mother," said Billy.

Father said to the children,
"Let's go and see the animals now.
It may be their lunch time."

"Yes! Yes!" said the children.
"Let's take the animals some peanuts."

They went to feed the animals
First they went to feed
the big elephant.
The children had some peanuts
for the big elephant.
They threw peanuts to the elephant.
The big elephant did not want
the peanuts.
He wanted to take a bath.
The big elephant wanted a big bath.
"Look! Look!" said Father.
"The elephant is going to take a bath!"

The elephant took water
in his long trunk.
He threw the water over his back.
The elephant took more water
in his long trunk
and threw it over his back.
He threw water over his back
and all around.
What a good bath the elephant had!

Then he saw the children.
The big elephant wanted to play.
He took more water in his trunk.

"Look out," said Father,
"or you will get a bath."

The elephant threw the water.
Ted and Jane ran just in time.

Mary said, "I got a bath.
See the water on my dress."

Billy said, "I got a bath, too."
Everyone laughed and laughed.
Ted and Jane said,
"We did not get a bath."

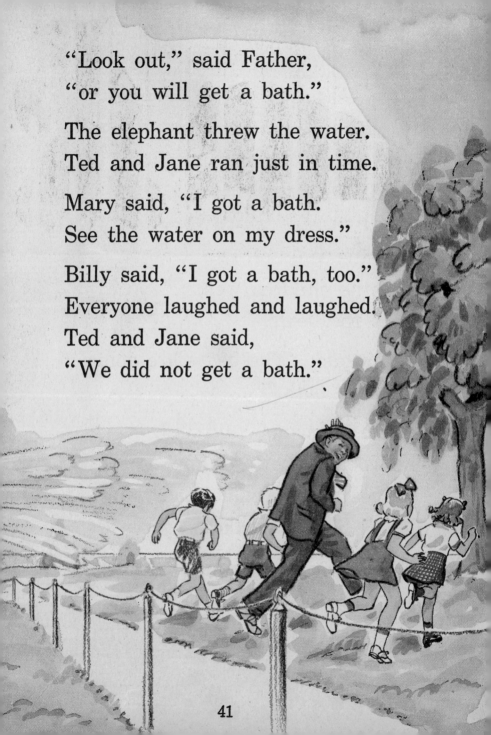

Then the children went
to see the bears.

Father said, "The bears are going
to take a bath."

"I like to swim," said Ted,
"and bears like to swim."
The bears came out of the water.
Shake! Shake! Shake!

Father said, "Look out,
or you will get a bath."
All the children ran just in time.
No one got a bath.

The bears saw the children.
Big father bear sat up
and held out his paw.
Mother bear sat up
and held out her paw.
Little baby bear sat up
and held out his paw.

"They want some peanuts," said Jane.

Father said, "Read that sign."

The sign said, "Do not feed the bears."

43

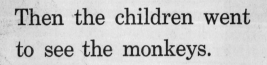

Then the children went
to see the monkeys.

"See the monkeys play!" said Ted.

The big, old monkey ran
after a little baby monkey.
The little baby monkey
could not get away.

"Now I have you,"
said the big, old monkey.
"You can not get away."

The monkeys saw the children.
The big, old monkey
held out his paw.

Ted threw some peanuts
to the big, old monkey.
Then the little baby monkey
held out his paw.

"I want some peanuts!"
said the little baby monkey.

Jane threw some peanuts
to the little baby monkey.

Then Father said,
"No more peanuts for the monkeys."

Then the children went to see
the baby animals in the Zoo.
First they saw a baby lion.

Jane said, "The baby lion looks
like a big kitten.
His paws look like my kitten's paws."

Mary said, "Look at this baby!
This baby looks like a kitten, too!
I want to play with him.
I want to take him home with me."

Father said, "That is not a kitten.
That is a baby tiger.
You could play with him, now,
but some day he will be too big
and strong."

Billy saw a baby kangaroo.
Billy said, "Look at baby kangaroo.
He is in his mother's pocket."
The children ran to see baby kangaroo.
He was in his mother's pocket!

Father said to the children,
"A baby kangaroo can not run.
Mother kangaroo has a big pocket.
Mother kangaroo puts her baby
in her pocket when she runs fast.
The baby kangaroo likes to ride
in his mother's pocket."

Billy said to Jane,
"Look at this baby.
This baby can not ride in a pocket.
This baby is too big for a pocket."

All the children ran to see
the great, big baby.
He was with his mother.

Father said, "Shall we take the
great, big baby home with us?"
The children laughed and laughed.

The children said good-by
to the Zoo and the Zoo animals.
This is what the children said:

"Good-by, good-by, good-by, Zoo.
Good-by, baby kangaroo,
Baby bear and tiger, too,
Baby kittens in the Zoo.
We like what the monkeys do.
Big, old elephant, we like you.
Good-by, good-by, good-by, Zoo."

At the Circus

One day Billy said to Jane,
"I saw the circus sign
in the grocery store.
There will be bears and elephants
in the circus."

Jane said,
"Yes, I saw that sign,
and I want to go to the circus."

All the children wanted to go
to the big circus.

Jane's mother said,
"Children, I will take you
to the circus on Saturday."

The children went to the circus
in the big, yellow bus.
When they came to the circus
they saw the big tent.
Near the big tent was a ticket man.

The ticket man said,
"Get your tickets here.
Get your tickets for the big show!
Get in line! Get in line!"

Jane's mother said to the man,
"I want five tickets."

The man gave her five tickets.
"One, two, three, four, five."

Mother said, "We will have
a short time to look around.
Let's see the little tents first.
Then we will go into the big tent."

MAIN ENTRANCE

Billy said, "I have ten cents.
Let's have some fun!"

Ted said, "I have ten cents."
Mary had ten cents,
and Jane had ten cents.

Jane's mother said,
"What do you want to do?"
They saw a sign that said,

LIONS AND BEARS

GET YOUR
TICKETS HERE

10¢ TO SEE THE LIONS AND BEARS 10¢

Jane said, "Let's go into this tent
and see the lions and bears."

Then Ted saw a sign that said,

Ted said, "Let's go into this tent and see the Strong Man."

Jane said, "I do not want to see a Strong Man."

Then they all saw this sign:

Billy said, "I want some lemonade.
I am not going to see the lions.
I am not going to see the bears.
I am not going to see the Strong Man,
I am going to get some lemonade
and peanuts."

The children said, "Come on!
Let's get some, too."

Everyone got some lemonade.
Everyone got some peanuts.

Then Jane's mother said,
"Here are your tickets.
One, two, three, four, five!
It is time for the circus, now."

They went into the big tent.

The elephants came
into the big tent.

"Look," said Billy.
"That elephant has his trunk
around the next elephant's tail.
The next elephant has his trunk
around the next elephant's tail."

Ted said, "See the next one!
And the next one!"
One, two, three, four, five.

The elephants did tricks.
One great, big elephant
put his trunk around a man.
Up, up, up went the man.
Then down, down, down he came.
The man was not afraid.
He was a circus man.
He liked to do tricks
with his big elephant.

The circus horses came in next.
Some horses were big
and some were little.
Some horses were white
and some were black.
Some horses were black and white.
The horses ran around and around.

A circus girl did tricks
on a horse's back.
A circus man jumped from one horse
to the next horse.
The circus man was not afraid.
The horses ran around and around.
They all did tricks.

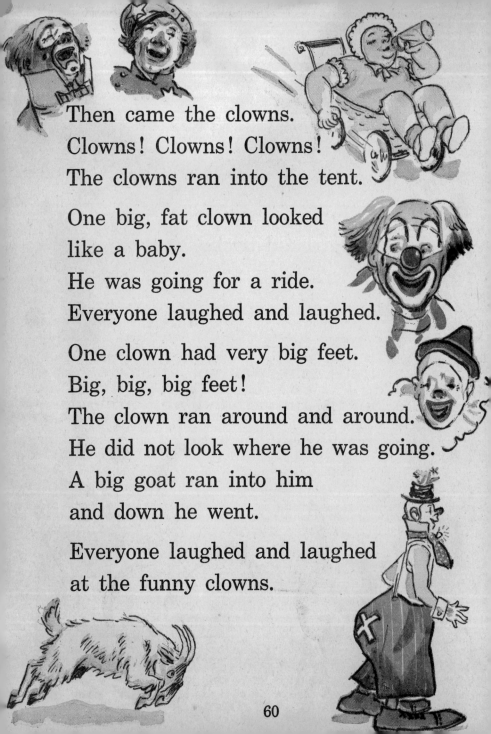

Then came the clowns.
Clowns! Clowns! Clowns!
The clowns ran into the tent.

One big, fat clown looked
like a baby.
He was going for a ride.
Everyone laughed and laughed.

One clown had very big feet.
Big, big, big feet!
The clown ran around and around.
He did not look where he was going.
A big goat ran into him
and down he went.

Everyone laughed and laughed
at the funny clowns.

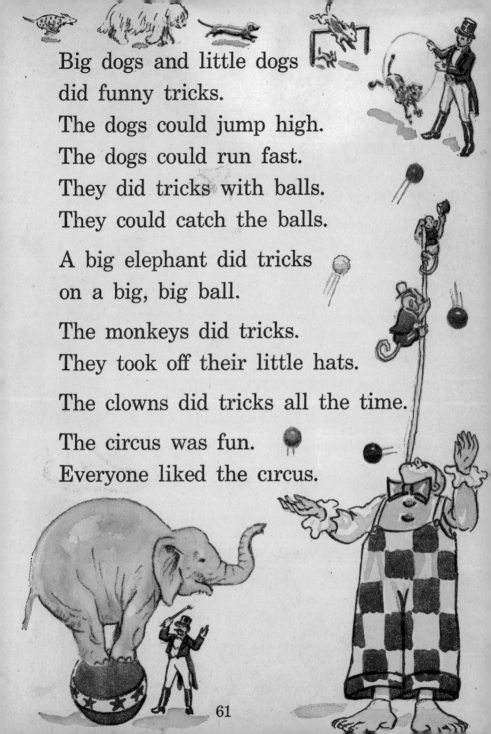

Big dogs and little dogs
did funny tricks.
The dogs could jump high.
The dogs could run fast.
They did tricks with balls.
They could catch the balls.

A big elephant did tricks
on a big, big ball.

The monkeys did tricks.
They took off their little hats.

The clowns did tricks all the time.

The circus was fun.
Everyone liked the circus.

After the big circus was over,
the children had a little circus.
The little circus was
in Billy's back yard.

Mary and Jane were circus girls.
Billy was a circus man.
Ted was a funny clown.
He had very big feet
like the clown in the big circus.

Ted's goat did tricks. Oh my!

Billy's dog did tricks. Oh my!

He jumped high and ran fast.

Mary's kitten was a circus lion.

The children who came to the circus
had a very good time.

Everyone was laughing all the time.

Everyone was talking all the time.

Fun at the Movies

One day Mary said to Jane,
"I want to go to the movies.
The movie is about Papa Penguin.
I know the story of Papa Penguin.
I read it in a library book.
I liked the story in the book.
Now I want to see the movie."

Jane said,
"I want to see that movie, too.
But I do not know the story.
Tell me about Papa Penguin."

Mary said,
"Papa Penguin looks like
a funny, little man.
I will tell you no more!
You must see the movie."

On Saturday the girls went
to see the movie about Papa Penguin.
Away went Mary and Jane
down the street to the movies!
There was the policeman
to help them cross the street.

Many children went down the street
to the movies.
The policeman helped
the children cross the street.

The children had a good time
at the movies.
Everyone laughed and laughed.

Jane said to Mary,
"That was a very good movie.
Papa Penguin is funny."

A Good Grocery Boy

One day after school Ted said,
"Father, may I help you
in the grocery store?"

Ted's father said, "Yes, Ted,
you may help me in the store."

Ted said to himself,
"Billy will come to the store.
Mary will come to the store.
Jane will come to the store.
I want to surprise them."

Ted's father asked,
"Can you make change?"

Ted said, "No, Father,
I can not make change."

Ted's father said,
"I will show you.
You put money in the box.
You take money out of the box."

Ted said to his father,
"Now I can make change!
I put money in the box.
Click! Click! Ring!
Then I take money out of the box.
Click! Click! Ring!
And there is the change!"

Mary came to the grocery store.
She said, "Oh, Ted, you look
like a grocery boy!"

Ted said, "I am a grocery boy.
May I help you, Mary?"
Ted helped Mary get what she wanted.
Mary gave Ted some money.
Ted put the money in the box.
Click! Click! Ring!
He took some money out.
Click! Click! Ring!
He gave Mary her change.

She said, "Thank you, Ted.
You are a very good grocery boy."

Jane came to the grocery store.
Ted helped Jane get what she wanted.

Jane gave him some money.
Click! Click! Ring!
Ted gave Jane her change.

Billy came to the grocery store.
Ted helped Billy get what he wanted.

Billy gave him some money.
Click! Click! Ring!
Ted gave Billy his change.
Ted helped his father
for a long, long time.

Father said to Ted,
"You are a good grocery boy.
There is something
in the box for you."
"Click! Click! Ring!"
said the money box.
Father gave Ted ten cents.

"This is for you!" said Father.

"Thank you, Father," said Ted.
"I like to help you."

Going to the Library

It was Saturday.
Mary went up to Jane's apartment.
Mary said to Jane,
"I want to go to the library.
Will you go with me?"

Jane said, "Oh, yes,
I want to go to the library, too.
I want to get the story
of Papa Penguin."

Mary said, "I want to find
a good book to take to school."

Mary and Jane went down the street
to the library.
Mary and Jane looked up the street.
They looked down the street.
The policeman helped them
cross the street.
It was a short walk
to the library.
They went into the library.
They saw a sign.

SILENCE

They did not talk in the library.
They went to Miss White.
Miss White helped Mary and Jane.
Miss White found good books for them.

Mary and Jane sat down
but they could not read.
Someone was laughing.
Someone was talking.
Someone was running around.
It was a little, little girl.
She could not read the sign.
Miss White went to the little girl.
She helped the little girl
find her mother.

Billy and Ted went to the library.
They saw the sign.
The boys saw Mary and Jane,
but they did not talk
to Mary and Jane.
They went to Miss White.

Billy said to Miss White,
"I want a book about Zoo animals."

Ted said, "I want a circus story."
Miss White helped Billy and Ted.
She found some good books
about Zoo animals.
She found some books about the circus.

Jane took home a book
about Papa Penguin.
Billy took a book about Zoo animals.
Ted took a book about the circus.
Mary took a book about farm children.

When the children went home,
they looked up the street.
They looked down the street.
The policeman helped them
cross the street.
When the children got home,
they read their library books.

The children took
their library books to school.
Mary had a story to tell
about the library.
She said to the children,
"Jane and I went to the library.
Someone was there
who could not read the sign.
Someone was laughing.
Someone was talking.
Someone was running.
It was a little girl."

Then Jane and Mary,
Billy and Ted read their books.
They read their library books
to all the children at school.
The children liked the books.
They liked the farm book best.
They said, "Farm children have fun.
It must be fun to live on a farm."

ON THE FARM

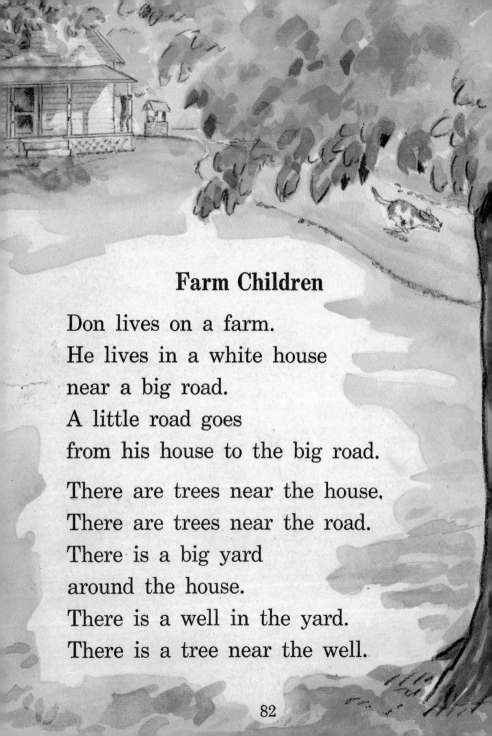

Farm Children

Don lives on a farm.
He lives in a white house
near a big road.
A little road goes
from his house to the big road.

There are trees near the house.
There are trees near the road.
There is a big yard
around the house.
There is a well in the yard.
There is a tree near the well.

Sue lives on the farm, too.
She lives in the white house
near the big road.

Sue and Don like the yard.
They play in the big yard.
Sometimes they climb the trees.
Sometimes they run down
the little road to the big road.
Sometimes they get water
from the old well.
Sue and Don like to live on a farm.

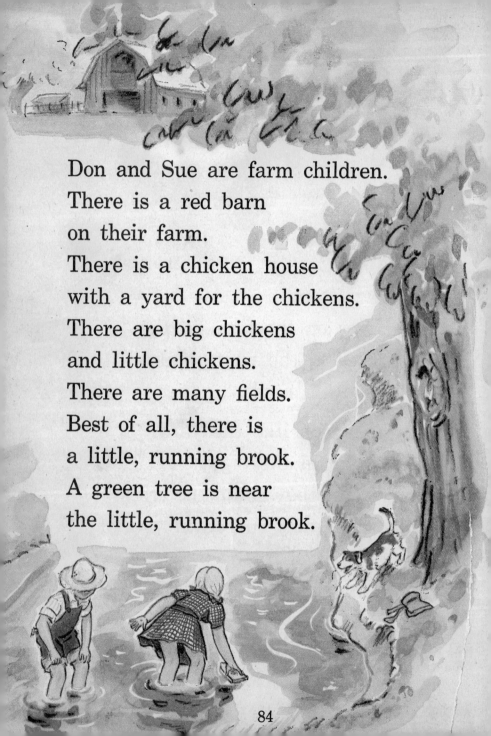

Don and Sue are farm children.
There is a red barn
on their farm.
There is a chicken house
with a yard for the chickens.
There are big chickens
and little chickens.
There are many fields.
Best of all, there is
a little, running brook.
A green tree is near
the little, running brook.

Don and Sue see farm horses
on the big road.
They see many cars on the big road.
They see many trucks on the big road.

A big, blue bus goes up the road
and down the road.

A policeman rides up the road
and down the road.
Up and down the road go the cars.
Up and down the road.
Up and down goes the policeman.
Up and down, up and down.

Their mail box is under a tree
near the big road.
There is a little flag
on the mail box.
The mail man comes up the road.
He comes in a car.
He puts mail in their box.
Then he puts up the little flag.
When the children see the little flag,
they know there is mail in the box.

Don and Sue look
for the mail man.
When they see him,
they run to the mail box.
They get the mail
for father and mother.

Sometimes Don and Sue put mail
in the box.
They put up the little flag.
Then the mail man knows
there is mail in the box.

When the flag is up,
there is mail in the box.

When the flag is down,
there is no mail in the box.

Don and Sue go to school.
They go to school in a yellow bus.
The big, yellow bus takes them
to school.
Don and Sue are gone all day.
They come home in the bus.

Mother looks for the big,
yellow school bus.
She is glad when it stops
at the little road.
She is glad to see Don and Sue
Don and Sue are glad to see
their mother.

Don and Sue are glad
when Saturday comes.
It is their play day.
They ride their horses.
Prince is Don's horse.
Tony is Sue's horse.
Don and Sue like to ride
to the next farm.
The children on the next farm hear
someone talking,
someone laughing,
someone running.

They call,
"Hello Don! Hello Sue!"

Fun on the Farm

One time Billy and Mary came
from the city.
They came to see Don and Sue
on the farm.
Billy said, "Oh, see the big barn!"
Mary said, "Let's go to the barn."

Sue called to the children,
"Come on!" and away they ran.
Don called to his dog, "Come on!"
Don's dog ran with the children.

Don said, "Let's feed the cows.
I have something in my pocket
for the cows."

Sue said, "Let's feed the horses.
I have something in my pocket
for Prince and Tony."
They ran around the big, red barn.

Just then a great big goat
came out of the barn.
Mary saw the great big goat.
Mary was afraid of the big goat.
Don held the goat and Mary ran.

Sue said to Mary, "Come with me.
We will go and feed my chickens.
You will see big chickens
and little chickens."

They ran to see the little chickens
and the hen's nest.

Mary said to Sue,
"I like the little yellow chickens."

Sue said,
"I like the black chickens best."

Don said to Billy, "Come down
to the brook and see my ducks.
You will see some big white ducks
and some little yellow ducks."

They went down to the brook
to see Don's ducks.
There were big white ducks
and little yellow baby ducks.

Billy said, "Look! Look!
See the little ducks swim!"

Fun in the Rain

One day Billy said,
"Look at the rain!
Now we can have no fun.
Rain, rain, go away!"

"Yes, we can have fun," said Don.
"This is a good day to fish.
Let's get some worms.
We will have to walk in the mud.
We will have to dig in the mud
for worms."

The boys went out in the rain.
"What are you going to do now?"
asked Billy.

"I am going to the field to dig
for worms," said Don.
Dig, dig, dig in the mud!
Dig, dig, dig in the mud!
"I see a worm," said Billy.
"And here are some more worms.
One, two, three, four, five."
Don put the worms in a can.

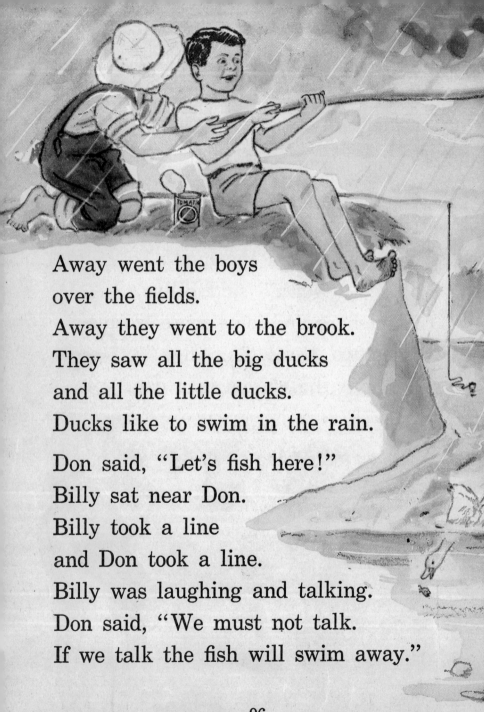

Away went the boys
over the fields.
Away they went to the brook.
They saw all the big ducks
and all the little ducks.
Ducks like to swim in the rain.

Don said, "Let's fish here!"
Billy sat near Don.
Billy took a line
and Don took a line.
Billy was laughing and talking.
Don said, "We must not talk.
If we talk the fish will swim away."

By and by, Billy said,
"There is something on my line."

Don said, "You have a fish."

Billy pulled and pulled.
"This must be a big fish," he said.
He pulled and pulled
and pulled and pulled.

Don said, "Let me help you.
I am big and strong."
Don and Billy pulled.
Up came something.
Billy did not have a big fish!
He had a big shoe!

By and by, Don said,
"There is something on my line."
He pulled and pulled
and pulled and pulled.
Up came a big fish.

Then Billy said,
"There is something on my line."
He pulled and pulled
and pulled and pulled.
Up came a big fish.

The boys ran up to Sue.

"Look at my fish,"
said Billy.
"Don's fish is not as long
as my fish."

"Look at my fish," said Don.
"Billy's fish is not as long
as my fish."

Sue said, "We will see."
She took Billy's fish
and she took Don's fish.

She said, "Billy's fish is
just as long as Don's fish.
Don's fish is just as long
as Billy's fish.
We have two big, long fish."

In the Barn

After dinner some boys came
to play with Don and Billy.
Some girls came
to play with Sue and Mary.

Don said, "Let's have some fun.
Let's climb up in the barn."

Away ran the children
to the big, red barn.
They climbed up in the big barn.

Don said, "I will be 'It.'
Go and hide.
No laughing, no talking,
or I will find you!"
The children ran to hide.

Don said, "5, 10, 15, 20."
Mary hid in the hay.

"25, 30, 35, 40."
Sue hid in the hay.

"45, 50, 55, 60."

Billy said to himself,
"Where shall I hide?"

"65, 70, 75, 80."

Then Billy had a big surprise!
Down he went into the cow's manger.

"85, 90, 95, 100," said Don.

Then he called,
"Ready or not, here I come."

Mary hid in the hay.
She hid near the hen's nest.
The hen did not like that.

"Cluck, cluck, cluck, cluck,"
said the hen.
"Cluck, cluck, cluck.
Get away! Get away from my nest."

Don said to himself,
"Hear that hen.
Who is near her nest?"

Don looked in the hay
near the hen's nest.
He found Mary.

Sue hid in the hay.
But she did not hide her toes.
Her toes stuck out.
Don saw her toes.
Don found Sue under the hay.
Don found all the children—
all but Billy.
Where was Billy?

Don could not find Billy.
He looked near the hen's nest.
He looked under the hay.
He looked high, he looked low.
High and low! High and low!
He looked here, he looked there.
Here and there! Here and there!

Where was Billy?
Billy hid in the cow's manger,
but he did not see the cow.
He pulled the hay over himself.
He could hear Don running around.
Don called, "Where is Billy?
I can not find Billy."
Billy laughed to himself.

Just then something
tickled Billy's toes.
Tickle! Tickle! Tickle!
Just then something said,
"Moo, moo, moo! Who are you?"
Billy was afraid.

"Oh, oh, oh!" called Billy.
"Don, come here! Come here!
Here I am in the manger!"

Don found Billy in the manger.
Don saw the cow.
He laughed and laughed.

Don said, "Do not be afraid
of the cow."

Billy said, "That big, old cow
tickled my toes."
The old cow said, "Moo, moo!"

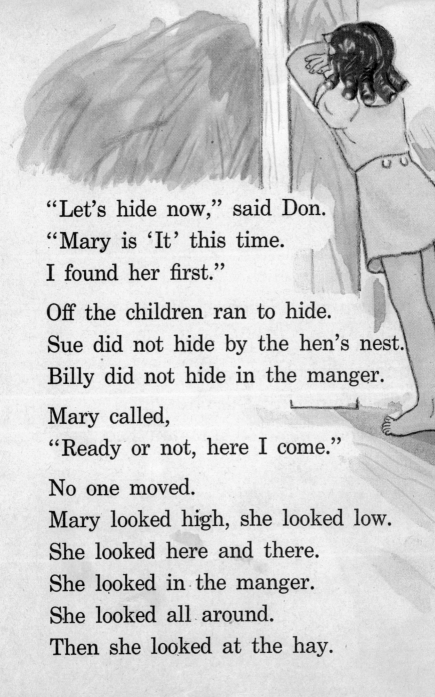

"Let's hide now," said Don.
"Mary is 'It' this time.
I found her first."

Off the children ran to hide.
Sue did not hide by the hen's nest.
Billy did not hide in the manger.

Mary called,
"Ready or not, here I come."

No one moved.
Mary looked high, she looked low.
She looked here and there.
She looked in the manger.
She looked all around.
Then she looked at the hay.

Mary looked and looked at the hay.
It moved a little.
It moved a little more.
Mary ran to the hay.
She pulled off some hay.
Someone's toes stuck out.
She pulled off more hay.
Someone's head stuck out.
She pulled off more and more hay!
There were all the children
under the hay!
Mary found all the children.
Everyone laughed and laughed.

Fun in the Sun

Next day the sun came out.
The children were glad
to see the sun.

The children said, "Good-by mud!
Good-by rain! Hello sun!
Now we can have more fun.
We had fun in the rain,
but we can have more fun in the sun!"

Don said, "I know what we can do.
Let's ride the horses."

The children said, "Yes!
Let's ride the horses."
All the children wanted
to ride the horses.
Away they went to the field.

Billy said to Don, "You ride first."

Don called Prince
and climbed on his back.
Away they went!
Around and around a big tree!
Around and around and around!

Don said, "This is like
the merry-go-round!
This is just like Play Park!"

Next Billy got on Prince.

Billy said, "Get up, Prince!"
But Prince did not go
where Billy wanted him to go.
Prince did not go
around and around the tree.
He went under the tree.
Down went Billy.

Don laughed and laughed.

Sue called Tony.
She climbed up on Tony.
She rode around and around
the big tree.

Then Mary climbed up on Tony.

Mary said, "Get up, Tony."
But Tony did not move.

Mary said, "Take me for a ride."
But Tony did not move.

"What shall I do?" asked Mary.

Sue said, "I know what we can do.
I will get on Tony.
Mary can ride with me."
Mary held on to Sue.

Don said, "I will get on Prince.
Billy can ride with me."
Billy held on to Don.

They got on the horses
and away they went!
Around and around the big tree!

"What fun," said Mary.
"This is just like the circus."

Sue said, "This is just like
the merry-go-round."

Up in a Tree

"Let's climb this tree," said Don.
"Who can climb the tree first?"

Everyone climbed the tree.

Don called out, "See where I am!
I can see the fields from here."

Then Billy called out,
"See where I am!
I can see the brook from here."

Sue said, "Look at me!"

Mary said, "Look at me!
We are all up, up, up in a tree."

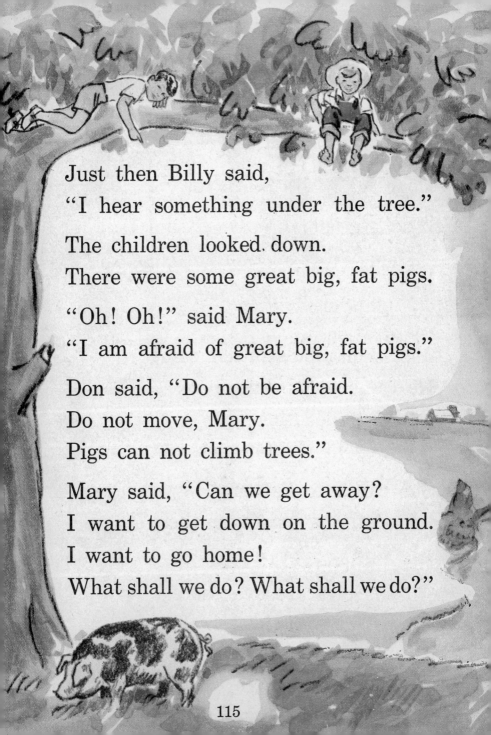

Just then Billy said,
"I hear something under the tree."

The children looked down.
There were some great big, fat pigs.

"Oh! Oh!" said Mary.
"I am afraid of great big, fat pigs."

Don said, "Do not be afraid.
Do not move, Mary.
Pigs can not climb trees."

Mary said, "Can we get away?
I want to get down on the ground.
I want to go home!
What shall we do? What shall we do?"

Just then Don's father came.
He came to feed the pigs.
Father called the pigs.
Away went the fat pigs.

Sue called to Father,
"Are all the pigs over there?"

Her father said, "Yes.
All the pigs are over here.
Climb down to the ground
and run, run, run!"

The children climbed down.
They ran out of the field.

Mary said to Don,
"I am glad your father came
and called the fat pigs away."

Billy was glad,
but he did not tell Mary.
He was afraid of the pigs, too,
but he did not want Mary to know it.

Bumblebees

The next day the children looked
for more fun.

Mary saw a swing in a big tree.

She said, "Let's swing!"

Don said, "You and Sue get
into the swing.
Billy and I will swing you."

First Don ran under the swing.
Then Billy ran under the swing.
The swing went up high.
Then the swing went down low.
High and low! High and low!
High and low! High and low!

Billy could hear a buzz.
"Buzz, buzz, buzz! Buzz! Buzz!"
It was in the ground.
Don could hear it, too.
Then he saw big bumblebees.
They came out of the ground.
"Buzz, buzz, buzz! Buzz! Buzz!"

"Stop the swing," he called.
The girls jumped out.

"Oh, oh, oh!" they called.
"Bumblebees are after us."

"Bumblebees are all around
my head," said Sue.

"They are all around my feet,"
said Mary. "What shall we do?
Help! Help! Help!"

"Run," said Don.
They all ran away
from the bumblebees.

"Where did the bumblebees
come from?" asked Mary.

Don said, "They came
from their nest in the ground.
We were on the bumblebees' nest.
They did not like big feet
on their nest.
If we do not walk on their nest
they will not come after us."

Mary said,
"I do not like bumblebees.
When the ground goes 'Buzz, buzz,'
I will run away very fast."

Down the Old Well

"What shall we do now?"
asked Billy.

"There is a funny Don
on this farm," said Don.
"Come with me, I will call to him."

The children went with Don
and Sue to the old well.

Don said, "Now you will hear
the funny Don.
If I call to Don in the well,
he will call to me.
Hello, Don! Hello!"

Then the children could hear,
"Hello, Don! Hello!"
It came up from the well.

"Is someone down there?"
asked Mary.

"There is a Mary in the well,"
said Don. "If you call to her,
she will call to you."

Mary called, "Hello, Mary!"
Up from the well came the call,
"Hello, Mary!"
"Who said that?" asked Mary.

Then Sue's mother came over
to the well.

She called down the well,
"Time for dinner!"
Up from the well came the call,
"Time for dinner!"

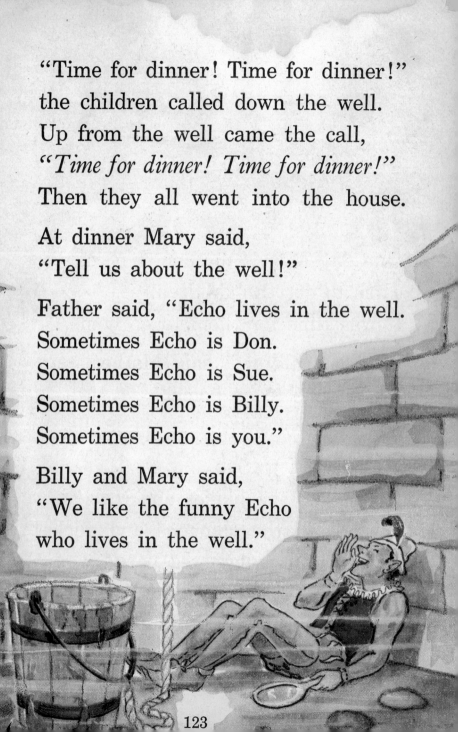

"Time for dinner! Time for dinner!"
the children called down the well.
Up from the well came the call,
"Time for dinner! Time for dinner!"
Then they all went into the house.

At dinner Mary said,
"Tell us about the well!"

Father said, "Echo lives in the well.
Sometimes Echo is Don.
Sometimes Echo is Sue.
Sometimes Echo is Billy.
Sometimes Echo is you."

Billy and Mary said,
"We like the funny Echo
who lives in the well."

One day Mary's mother
came to get the children.
It was time for them to go home.

"Come, children," said Mother.
"It is time to go home."

Billy and Mary said good-by
to Don and to Sue.
Good-by to the horses and cows!
Good-by to the chickens and ducks!
Good-by to the big, red barn!
Good-by to the big, green trees!
Good-by to the little, blue brook!
Good-by, good-by to everyone!

Then Billy said,
"There is one more good-by!"
He ran back to the old well.
"Good-by, good-by," said Billy.
"Good-by, good-by," said Echo.

I Live in the City

I like to play in my yard.
I like to ride my bicycle.
I like to go to the movies.
I like to go to the Zoo.

I like to play in the park.
I like to read in the library.
I like to go to the grocery store.
I like to go to the circus.

I like to go to school.
I like to get the mail.
I like to see the policeman.
I like to see the cars go by
on the city streets.

What do you like to do
in the city?

I Live on the Farm

I like to play in the fields.
I like to race with my dog.
I like to climb trees.
I like to fish in the brook.

I like to dig in the mud.
I like to swing high and low.
I like to ride the horses.
I like to feed the chickens.

I like to go to school.
I like to get the mail.
I like to see the policeman.
I like to see the cars go by
on the big road.

What do you like to do
on the farm?

The total number of words used in this First Reader is 311. The following list contains 161 new words used in this First Reader that were not taught in the Pre-Primer and Primer. 136 are in the Thorndike list, 137 are in the I.K.U. list, and 124 are in the Gates list. No word is used less than 6 times. Average repetition is 22.7.

5–7	24 ticket	43 held	85
8 city	cents	paw	86 under
lives	horses	baby	flag
Ted	lions	44 old	87
park	bears	could	88 glad
street	25 rode	45	89 Prince
brick	white	46 strong	Tony
just	sat	47 kangaroo	hear
number	high	pocket	call
9 Mary	tiger	48 great	90
Jane	around	49	91 cows
apart-	26 from	50 circus	92 hen's
ment	27	51 tent	nest
know	28 who	near	93 ducks
their	first	line	94 rain
10 many	bath	52–56	fish
11 goes	splash	57 tricks	worms
by	29 called	afraid	dig
stop	30 sand	58–59	mud
ride	over	60 clowns	95–96
12 truck	some	very	97 pulled
13 yard	himself	61 off	98
14 must	toes	62–63	99 as
when	stuck	64 Papa	100 dinner
cross	31 everyone	Penguin	climbed
policeman	more	65 helped	hide
15 them	home	66	101 hid
16 mail	32 tickled	67 change	hay
17	got	68 money	manger
18 store	33	click	102 cluck
grocery	34 Zoo	ring	103
Saturday	sun	69–72	104 low
helps	35 asked	73 found	105 moo
19 movies	lunch	74 someone	106
funny	36 shall	running	107 moved
animals	or	75	108–114
20 library	37 sticks	76 farm	115 pigs
21 sign	long	77–81	ground
where	if	82 Don	116–117
took	38 lemonade	road	118 bumble-
22 merry-go-	time	trees	bees
round	peanuts	well	swing
oh	39 feed	83 Sue	119 buzz
swim	elephant	sometimes	120–122
23 am	threw	climb	123 Echo
short	40 trunk	84 barn	124–127
fat	41–42	chicken	
		field	
		brook	